ROY
RHYMER
15
Royal
Infirm.
Cathedral of
Mungo
Necropolis

STRATHCLYDE REGIO
AND GLASGOW
DISTRICT COUNCIL
NITY CHARGES (POLL TAX) D
1989/90
ARE LIAB

NIE NEWS
s of Spinbinnie Hospital)

CAMO

HUMFRY
bOGart
Like

'HE THINKS HE
BOGA

THE
OGU

OGANO

Bogie M

TILIDOM 8 30

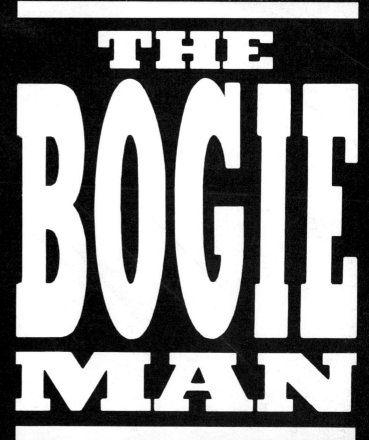

THE BOGIE MAN

Published by John Brown Publishing Limited, The Boathouse,
Crabtree Lane, London, SW6 8NJ. The Bogie Man is copyright ©
1991 John Wagner, Alan Grant and Robin Smith. This edition
copyright © 1991 John Brown Publishing. All rights reserved. No
part of this book may be reproduced, except for review purposes,
without the written permission of the authors and publisher. The
characters, incidents and names mentioned in this book are
entirely fictional. First serialised in the United Kingdom by
Fatman Press, 1989. First printing by John Brown Publishing,
August 1991. Printed and bound in Great Britain.

SCRIPT
**JOHN WAGNER &
ALAN GRANT**
ART
ROBIN SMITH
LETTERING
BAMBOS

THE BOGIE MAN

FAREWELL MY LOONEY

5

♪ SHOULD AULD ACQUAINTANCE BE FORGOT, FOR AULD LANG SYNE... ♪

FOR AULD LANG SYNE, MY DEAR, FOR AULD LANG SYNE - WE'LL TAK A CUP O' KINDNESS YET FO-OR AULD LA-ANG SYNNNNE!

HAPPY NEW YEAR!

ANOTHER YEAR IN, EH, HUEY? AYE... WONDER WHAT THE NEW YIN'LL BRING FOR US AW, EH?

I'LL TELL YE - MAIR BAMPOTS.

COME RAIN, HAIL OR SHINE THERE'S WAN THING YE CAN BE SURE OF IN THIS PLACE - MAIR BAMPOTS!

HOW DO THEY CELEBRATE HOGMANAY IN YOUR COUNTRY, DOCTOR ALUM?

SAME BLOODY WAY THEY DO HERE, YOU EEJIT. I COME FRAE ABERDEEN!

HOW'RE YE GETTIN' HAME, HEN?

QUIET, PLEASE!

DOCTOR BRANCH WANTS TO SAY A FEW WORDS!

FIRST OF ALL I'M SORRY YOU'VE HAD TO BE ON DUTY TONIGHT. SOMEONE HAS TO DO IT, AND UNFORTUNATELY THIS YEAR IT'S US.

I WANT TO THANK YOU FOR ALL YOUR HARD WORK AND WISH YOU THE VERY BEST FOR THE YEAR TO COME.

YOUR VERY GOOD HEALTH!

GOOD ON YE, OLLIE!

HAPPY NEW YEAR, DOCTOR!

HERE'S TAE US - WHA'S LIKE US?

6

HAPPY
NEW YEAR,
MR –

NO' THE NIGHT – NO'
ON HOGMANAY OF
AW NIGHTS..!

AW,
NAWWW!

YA DAFT GALOOT!
WHAT D'YE WANT TO
GO AN' DO A THING
LIKE THIS –

9

AS I WAS SLOWLY PASSING AN ORPHAN HOME ONE DAY...

...I STOOD THERE FOR A MOMENT JUST TO WATCH THE CHILDREN PLAY — ALONE A BOY WAS STANDING...

≡SNIFF≡ AH ALWAYS GREET WHEN THEY PLAY THIS YIN!

HOW'RE YE GETTIN' HAME, HEN?

-TURNED WITH EYES THAT COULD NOT SEE AND HE BEGAN TO CRY ♪

I'M NO-BODY'S CHI-ELD! NO-BODY'S CHI-ELD! ♪

I'M LIKE A FLOW-WERRR, JUST GROWING WI-ELD! ♪

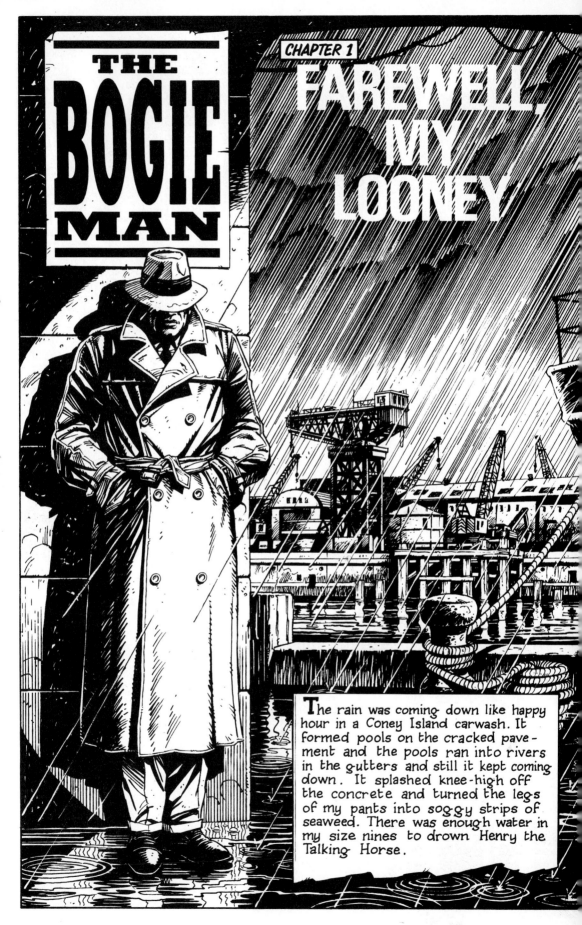

THE BOGIE MAN

FAREWELL, MY LOONEY

The rain was coming down like happy hour in a Coney Island carwash. It formed pools on the cracked pavement and the pools ran into rivers in the gutters and still it kept coming down. It splashed knee-high off the concrete and turned the legs of my pants into soggy strips of seaweed. There was enough water in my size nines to drown Henry the Talking Horse.

Across the river I could hear the eerie wail of a siren. Some lunatic had taken a powder from the asylum. He'd chosen a bad night.

But then I guess lunatics can't pick their weather, any more than guys in my line.

I'm a private eye.

I was waiting for a Joe by the name of McGurk - Joe McGurk. At least he was when I knew him.

A Joe with a long past and a potentially short future if he didn't sing the kind of song I like to hear.

OH WE'RE NO' AWA-A TAE BIDE AWA

OH, WE'RE NO' AWA-A TAE LEAVE YE —

C'MON, RA BHOYSSS!

AW - HEY!

HAPPY NEW YEAR, JIMMY!

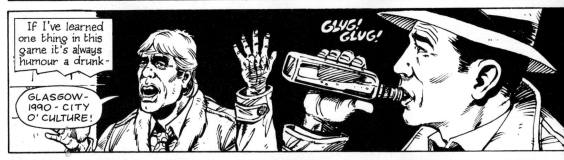

YOU'RE ALREADY —IT.

ALWAYS WERE THE SHARP ONE, JOE.

I gave him the long, slow once-over. He'd changed some since I'd last seen him, but there was no mistaking that scar.

SO HOW YOU BEEN, JOE?

YA BIG YANKEE BALLOON! WHEN AH GET OOTA HERE—

...H, I THINK YOU'VE GOT —HE WRONG MAN...

NO, I GOT THE RIGHT MAN, JOE. I OUGHTA KNOW—I GAVE YOU THAT LITTLE SCAR IN A BOTTLE FIGHT IN DETROIT!

—ETROIT? —UT I'VE —EVER—

I'd had enough yakking. There was only one kind of language the McGurks ever understood—

GNNGHHH!

REMEMBER ME NOW, JOE?

UNNH!

RIGHT, FERRIT FACE! I'M GAUNY DUNT YER PUSS!

KLUNG!

AHHHH!

LET'S CUT THE PHONEY BALONEY! YOU KNOW WHY I'M HERE. WHERE'S THE FAT MAN?

WHU-WHO-?

DON'T PLAY DUMB WITH ME, JOE! THE *FAT MAN* - THE TWO-TON LUMPA BLUBBER BUSTED YOU OUTA SAN QUENTIN - THE SAME ONE HIRED YOU TO STEAL THE *BIRD*-!

I - I SWEAR I DON'T KNOW WHAT YOU'RE TALKING ABOUT!

IT'S JUST NO USE BEING NICE TO SOME FOLK, HUH, JOE?

PLEASE, YOU'RE MAKING A MISTAKE-

THE ONLY MISTAKE I MADE WAS LEAVIN' YOU ALIVE IN DETROIT!

I could see he wasn't going to sing. Too frightened of the Fat Man.

WHAXK!

I went through his pockets. Joe'd got himself a complete change of I.D.

SOMEBODY PAID PLENTY FOR THIS - AND IT SURE WASN'T MEDICARE.

There was one item of interest - a matchbook for a nightspot. One of those swanky joints where they serve you beer with a cocktail stick and the waitresses wear fluffy tails.

TOMMY TROTTERS GLASGOW

OHH, MA HEID - !

It wasn't much to go on but it might just give me a line on the Fat Man. If I could find Fatso you could bet your bottom dollar the Big Bird wouldn't be far away.

fsssttu

Me, I was fresh out of dollars.

I was betting my life.

RIGHT, YOUSE!

IT'S LALDY TIME!

THIS IS THE ROOM, MR. ER...?

NO NAMES, GRANDMA. SAFER FOR BOTH OF US THAT WAY.

It was a crummy little box in a crummy little flophouse, but I needed a place to hole up. At least the bed was clean and there weren't any bugs —

—or if there were the management was paying them hush money.

THAT WILL BE TWENTY POUNDS, IN ADVANCE. THAT INCLUDES BREAKFAST, OF COURSE.

PORRIDGE OR KIPPERS?

PORRIDGE OR KIPPERS?

THAT SOUNDS LIKE SOME KINDA DISEASE, SISTER. BETTER GET IT LOOKED AT.

AN' WHILE YOU'RE AT IT YOU CAN DISABUSE YOURSELF OF ANY NOTION I'M PAYIN' TWENNY FINS FOR THIS TWO-BIT LITTLE RAT TRAP.

I'LL GIVE YOU A BUCK A DAY, PAYABLE A WEEK NEXT THURSDAY. TAKE IT OR LEAVE IT.

SSCCREEEE!

SWEET MOTHERA LARRY!

GEDDOWN, FROGFACE!

WH- WHAT IS IT?

THE *FAT MAN'S* GOONS! DUNNO HOW, BUT THEY'VE FOUND ME!

QUICK - YOU GOT A *PIECE*?

A PIECE..? D'YOU MEAN A - *SANDWICH*?

FOR PETE'S SAKE, GRANDMA - A *ROD*! A *HEATER*! A *GUN*!

OH MICHTY ME! I-IS THERE GOING TO BE SHOOTING?

NOT IF I CAN HELP IT!

If they caught me unarmed they'd be playing the Stars and Stripes on my ribs with .38 calibre dum-dums — and that's one tune I never want to hear again.

CHANCES ARE THEY'VE GOT THE BACK WAY COVERED.

CRAASH!

MICHTY ME!

ANYBODY ASKS, I WA NEVER HERE. SAVVY

MICHTY ME!

24

25

DO YE WANT ME TAE TAKE MA CLAES AFF AN' GIE YE A WEE KEEK?

GIVE US A BREAK, HEN. I'VE JUST HAD MY SUPPER.

HERE! YE CANNAE LOCK ME UP! I'M A FAMOUS TV PERSONALITY—

IAN! HELP!

IIIAAANNNNN!

FANDABBADOZEY!

I DUNNO, GEORGE, ONE NIGHT OF THE YEAR THE WHOLE TOWN GOES CRAZY! EVERYBODY AN' HIS GRANNY ON THE BATTER—MAIR NUTS THAN K.P!

YOU'D THINK THE WEATHER WOULD KEEP THEM IN.

DETECTIVE SERGEANT URE?

WANTED

I'M DOCTOR BRANCH, FROM GREENOCK.

I SEE YOU BROUGHT THE RAIN!

I SPOKE TO YOU EARLIER ON THE PHONE.

BRANCH... BRANCH...OH, AYE, THE ASYLUM. YOU'VE GOT A LOONEY ON THE LOOSE.

I WOULDN'T PUT IT QUITE LIKE THAT, SERGEANT, BUT YES, UNFORTUNATELY, ONE OF OUR PATIENTS HAS ESCAPED.

FINLAY! WILL YOU STOP HIM HUMPIN' THAT COFFEE MACHINE! WE'VE GOT TO DRINK THAT STUFF!

VENDO

SORRY ABOUT THAT, DOCTOR.

SO - WHAT DIFFERENCE WILL ONE *MORE* NUT MAKE IN GLASGOW TONIGHT ?

YOU'D BETTER READ HIS FILE.

RIGHT, TAKE A PEW.

CLUNIE...FRANCIS FORBES CLUNIE... COMMITTED OCTOBER '86 - DUH DAH DUH DAH - SEVERE PERSONALITY DISORDER -

THIS IS ALL A BIT TECHNICAL AT THIS TIME OF NIGHT, DOCTOR. SUPPOSE YOU TELL ME - WHAT MAKES YOU THINK HE'D COME TO GLASGOW ?

HE'S A CREATURE OF THE CITY - THE BRIGHT LIGHTS, THE EXCITEMENT. HE'D BE DRAWN HERE LIKE A MAGNET.

IS HE DANGEROUS ?

HE MAY BE.

MAY BE ?

WELL... PROBABLY.

PROBABLY ?

IT DEPENDS...

YOU SEE, MR. CLUNIE SUFFERS FROM... AN EXTREME AND UNUSUAL *DELUSION* THAT MAKES HIS BEHAVIOUR RATHER... *UNPREDICTABLE.*

IN WHAT WAY ?

HE THINKS HE'S *HUMPHREY BOGART.*

There was only one way to figure it. Joe McGurk must've recovered and tailed me. He'd tipped the Fat Man and Fats hadn't wasted any time. That big tub of blubber had a lot of friends in this burg.

I could see them now, dishing out my mugshot in every sleazy bar and run-down pool room in the city. Every piece of lowlife would be crawling out of their holes with guns in their mitts and my blood on their minds.

H. CALLAGHAN
SPORTING GOODS

Just back on the job and already I'd made my first mistake. I should have killed that scarfaced geek when I had the chance. I'd know better next time.

As long as I was out in the open without artillery I was a sitting duck.

NEXT-DAY DELIVERIES
"We drive by night!"

Fabrini Bros.

IT'S FUNNY, HE LOOKED LIKE THAT OLD MOVIE STAR — YOU KNOW, THE HAT AND THE TRENCHCOAT?

BOGIE — THAT'S THE ONE.

BOGART?

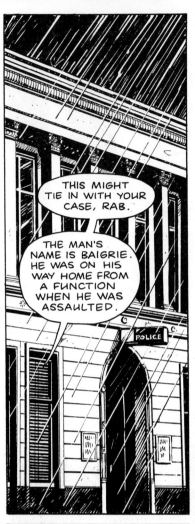

THIS MIGHT TIE IN WITH YOUR CASE, RAB.

THE MAN'S NAME IS BAIGRIE. HE WAS ON HIS WAY HOME FROM A FUNCTION WHEN HE WAS ASSAULTED.

POLICE

HE CALLS ME OVER, ASKS FOR A LIGHT — BUT THE GUY'S ALREADY SMOKING, YOU KNOW?

THEN HE STARTS TALKIN' CRAZY — SAYS I'M CALLED McGURK AND I KNOW WHERE SOME FAT MAN IS.

I TOLD HIM, I DON'T KNOW ANY FAT MEN — I'VE NEVER BEEN TO DETROIT. IT DOESN'T MAKE A BLIND BIT OF DIFFERENCE — NEXT THING I KNOW HE'S GIVING ME THE GRAEME SOUNESS!

BAD NEWS, DOC?

THE WORST, I'M AFRAID.

HE'S ON A JOB.

SORRY?

PRIVATE EYE.

HE'S BEGUN TO FABRICATE A WHOLE CASE. BUILDING IT UP AS HE GOES ALONG. ANY INNOCENT PARTY CAN BE SUCKED IN.

EACH NEW ENCOUNTER - EACH NEW "CLUE" - WILL BE TWISTED AND WOVEN INTO THE FABRIC OF HIS DELUSION.

AND CLUNIE ACTUALLY *BELIEVES* THIS STORY HE'S MAKING UP?

Fabrini Bros.

VRMM!

NOT CLUNIE - *BOGIE.*

HGV174W

CRASSSHHHH!!!!

CLUNIE NO LONGER EXISTS.

UNLESS THE *BOGIE MAN* IS FOUND — AND QUICKLY — YOU'LL HAVE MAYHEM ON THE STREETS OF GLASGOW!

CHAPTER 2

THE TREASURE OF THE FORD SIERRA

I could have been in L.A., browning like a prawn on Malibu. I could have been down Rio way, living it up in the Copacabana with a dusky lovely dangling from each arm.

I could have been in New York - London - Gay Paree. I could have been in Hoboken, for that matter.

But I wasn't. I was here.

11 a.m., Glasgow - on a morning grey and bloated as a month-old corpse. And for the thousandth time I asked myself what I was doing in this one-horse little burg.

But I knew. The Fat Man was in town. And in my experience that meant the Big Bird was here too.

I'd been holed up in this exclusive little hostelry for two days under the name of Miles Archer, my late partner. That was a clue even Fatso ought to get.

RAP RAP!

His goons had tried to hit me once. I knew they'd come again.

Now I was packing, I was ready for them.

BAP!

UNGGG!

YOU GOT *FIVE SECONDS* TO TELL ME WHO *SENT* YA, PUNK — AN' I WARN YOU, I'M A FAST COUNTER!

ONETWOTHREEFOURFIVE!

TOO *LATE*, PUNK. YOU'RE *MEAT*!

P-P-PLEASE! R-ROOM SERVICE — I'M ROOM SERVICE!

YEAH, YOU'RE ROOM SERVICE LIKE I'M A CHINEE WRESTLER'S JOCK STRAP!

A B-BOTTLE OF JACK DANIELS—CIGARETTES! YOU ORDERED THEM— REMEMBER?

SO I DID.

NO HARD FEELIN'S, KID. CAN'T BE TOO CAREFUL, HUH?

PAT PAT!

IS... IS THAT THING FOR REAL?

FULLA QUESTIONS, AREN'T YOU, KID? SOMEONE PAYIN' YA TO ASK 'EM—THAT IT?

N-NO, SIR! HONEST!

YIN' LITTLE RUNT! THINK I AVEN'T NOTICED THE WAY OU BEEN CHECKIN' EVERY-THING WITH THOSE HIFTY LITTLE PEEPERS?

HOW MUCH IS FATS PAYIN' YOU TO CASE THE JOINT?

NOTHING! HONEST!

He could've been on the level. But like Miles used to say— "Never trust a kid with shifty peepers." I debated plugging him then and there; I could use the pillow to muffle the shot.

But what the hell— I had to sleep on the thing.

Besides, the kid had brought me a bottle of Jack Daniels, and in my book that ain't a shooting offence.

C-CAN I GO NOW?

YANK!

YOU'RE GOIN' NOWHERE, KID. YOU'VE SEEN TOO MUCH.

SIDDOWN!

TIE YOURSELF UP!

NO! DINNAE YOU LEAVE ME WI' THIS BEAST!

BRANCH SPEAKING!

RAB URE HERE, DOCTOR.

SERGEANT URE? YOU'VE *FOUND* HIM, THEN?

I'M AFRAID NOT.

POLICE

THERE WAS A ROBBERY NIGHT BEFORE LAST, A GUN SHOP NEAR THE CITY CENTRE. SOMEBODY DROVE A LORRY THROUGH THE WINDOW. I'VE JUST HAD THE REPORT BACK...

THE FINGERPRINTS BELONG TO YOUR *BOGIE MAN*.

YOU MEAN - HE HAS A GUN?

A ·38 SPECIAL REVOLVER AND A HUNDRED ROUNDS OF AMMUNITION ARE MISSING.

OH DEAR.

WE ALSO FOUND THE MAN WHO GAVE HIM THE LIFT FROM GREENOCK. CLUNIE CRACKED HIM OVER THE HEAD, STOLE HIS CLOTHES AND THIRTY POUNDS IN CASH.

SO I'VE A LUNATIC LOOSE ON THE STREETS WITH A GUN - AND NO IDEA WHAT HE'S GOING TO DO NEXT.

I NEED SOME HELP ON THIS, DOCTOR. SOMEBODY WHO KNOWS HIM, WHO CAN PREDICT HIS POSSIBLE ACTIONS.

NOBODY KNOWS THE *BOGIE MAN* BETTER THAN YOU.

HERE! IS THAT NOT WEE TAM SINCLAIR DRIVIN' THE CASTLEMILK STAGECOACH?

I THOUGHT HE WAS BANNED?

HE IS. 'S AWRIGHT THOUGH – HE'S GOT A SHOT O' HIS BRITHER'S LICENCE.

OH.

IS HIS BROTHER NOT BANNED, TOO?

THAT'S THE LORRY THERE, MR. McCURDIE.

TUT TUT TUT TUT!

MR. McCURDIE, WE CAN –

NO, NO!

NO NEED TO EXPLAIN, GENTLEMEN. I UNDERSTAND PERFECTLY.

YOUSE ARE A PAIR O' BLOODY *EEJITS!*

WE - WE'RE AFFY SORRY, MR. McCURDIE--

IT WAS DARK. IT LOOKED LIKE THE RIGHT LORRY--

IS THAT A FACT?

WELL, GENTLEMEN, HAD YOU BUT TAKEN THE TROUBLE TO CHECK YOU MIGHT HAVE NOTICED A FEW SMALL BUT SIGNIFICANT DETAILS...

POINT ONE - IT IS, IS IT NOT, A *REFRIGERATED* LORRY?

NOW CORRECT ME IF I AM WRONG, BUT TO THE BEST OF MY KNOWLEDGE YOUR NORMAL VIDEO DOES NOT REQUIRE REFRIGERATION.

BUT, MR. McCURD--

POINT *TWO*-

AND HERE AGAIN YOU'LL PUT ME STRAIGHT IF I'M MISTAKEN - BUT UNLESS THEY'VE CHANGED THE LANGUAGE TOTALLY SINCE I WAS AT SCHOOL, T-A-R-T-A-N-BLOODY-T-U-R-K-E-Y DOES NOT SPELL *HITACHI!*

NOW, AM I RINGING ANY BELLS HERE?

MR. McC--

NO!

POINT *THREE* - AND HERE, BOYS, I THINK WE HAVE THE CLINCHER -

THANK YOU, AIRCHIE.

LISSEN - I KNOW WE GOT IT WRANG, MR. McCURDIE, B-BUT WHAT'S THE DIFFERENCE? I MEAN, VIDEOS - TURKEYS - YOU CAN GET RID O' THEM!

AYE, LIKE YE ALWAYS DO. NAE TOTHER A BA', EH?

IS THAT A FACT?

IN CASE IT HAD ESCAPED YOUR NOTICE IT'S TWO DAYS EFTER NEW YEAR. EVERYBODY AND HIS AUNTIE HAS BEE EATIN' TURKEY SINCE CHRISTMAS.

THE WHOLE O' SCOTLAND HAS TURKEY COMIN' OOT ITS EARS! NAEBODY - BUT NAEBODY - WANTS TO SEE ANOTHER TURKEY FOR AT LEAST ANOTHER YEAR!

AND YOU'RE TELLIN' ME I CAN GET RID O' THEM?

AIRCHIE - WOULD YOU HAPPEN TO HAVE YOUR BASEBALL BAT ABOOT YOUR PERSON?

RIGHT HERE, MR. MAC!

NAME YOUR LIMB, SIR!

I WAS THINKING OF THE SKULL, ACTUALLY.

IN THE NAME O' THE WEE MAN - PLEASE DON'T DO THIS TAE US, MR. McCURDIE!

C'M'OAN, GIE US A BREAK! IT'S THE SEASON O' GOODWILL ANNAT!

AN' - AN' WE'VE NO' EVEN FINISHED FIXIN' YOUR WIFE'S CAR YET!

6 o'clock came and went, and still no sign of Fats. Reception called looking for their trolley-boy. I denied all knowledge and ordered dinner for two.

Guess it should've been. for three.

Another hour and I'd had it with waiting. I'd been cooped up for two days, and I was getting itchy. If Fats wasn't going to come to me, I was going to have to find him.

TAXI!

I only had one clue to go on- a matchbook from some swanky nightspot I'd taken from Joe McGurk.

TOMMY TROTTER'S, AN' DON'T SPARE THE HORSES!

GLAD YOU COULD MAKE IT, DOCTOR BRANCH.

PLEASE- CALL ME *OLIVE*.

OLIVE?

OLIVE BRANCH..?

I'M AFRAID SO. ONE OF THE DRAWBACKS OF PACIFIST PARENTS.

NEVER MIND, IT COULD'VE BEEN WORSE. COULD'VE BEEN *TWIGGY*.

KEEP THIS UP, SERGEANT, AND IT'S GOING TO BE A VERY SHORT DINNER.

The cab driver had ears like baseball mitts. Every time he turned his head, I thought he was hanging a right. With a little more effort he could probably have flown us there.

WAIT HERE.

With ears like that, far as I was concerned the creep could wait till Doomsday.

I checked my piece and sized up Tommy Trotter's. Underneath its bright facade it was just another sleazy dive. Probably it'd seen better days. But if it had, my bet was they were never very good.

TOMMY TROTTER'S

Inside I gave it the once-over. If there was a face I recognised, I didn't recognise it yet. I slid up to the bar and ordered three fingers of rye...

I'VE NO' SEEN YOU IN HERE AFORE, BUT.

I'VE BEEN AWAY.

THE *BAR-L* ?

BEL-AIR, SISTER. NEW YORK—L.A. CASABLANCA. WHEREVER THE ACTION IS.

She was built, this babe. Hair the colour of molten honey — more curves than the Pasadena Turnpike. Another time, another place, me and her could've made the earth move. But I was on a case —

I'M LOOKIN' FOR A LITTLE INFORMATION, DOLL. LIKE WHAT TIME DOES THE *FAT MAN* GET IN ?

FAT MAN ?

WHIT FAT MAN ? THERE'S QUITE A *FEW* COMES IN HERE...

I S'POSE BIG WILLIE MUST BE THE FATTEST... AYE, *BIG WILLIE BROON.*

COULD BE MY MAN. WHAT TIME YOU EXPECTIN' HIM ?

OCH, HE'S NO' BEEN IN HERE FOR WEEKS. THE WAY I HEARD IT, HE'S GOT SO FAT HE CANNAE GET OOT THE HOOSE!

The Fat Man was too smart to eat himself into a corner like that. It had to be a ploy. Gutman was trying to lure me to *him*.

DINNAE LIKE THIS, UGGIE. WHIT IF MR. McCURDIE FINDS OOT WE'RE USIN' HIS WIFE'S CAR?

BUT HE'LL NO' FIND OOT! WE'LL HAVE IT BACK BY MORNIN', AN' A FEW QUID IN OOR POCKETS, TAE BOOT!

YOUSE WAIT HERE AN' WATCH FOR POLIS. I'LL NO' BE LONG!

If I was going to walk into the Fat Man's trap, I wanted a few more answers first — and I had a feeling Cutesy behind the bar knew more than she was telling.

THIS BROON — HE HAVE A GUNSEL WITH HIM? LITTLE RAT-FACE, NAME OF WILMER?

NA-AW.

I THINK HE WAS MAIRRIT, RIGHT ENOUGH — BUT SHE WUZNAE CA'ED WILMA.

YOU KNOW, YOUSE LOOK LIKE SOMEBODY...

I JUST CANNAE THINK, BUT! IT'S SOMEBODY AFF THE TELLY, ISN'T IT ?

DINNAE TELL ME NOW! IT'S NO' KOJAK ... NAW, YON ITHER WAN —

BOGART ?

DIRK BOGARDE ?

DINNAE BE DAFT! YE DINNAE LOOK A BIT LIKE HIM !

A piano started up in the corner and I ordered another shot. I was starting to get a tingle at the base of my spine — an itch I couldn't scratch.

I'VE GOT A LITTLE SOMETHIN' HERE MIGHT INTEREST YOU, JIMMY...

And then I heard the magic words —

JEEZ-OH! THAT'S A RIGHT BIG BIRD!

IT'S A STOATER, HEN!

ONE SIDE, STARCHY!

BAPP!

EVERYBODY FREEZE!

THE BIG BIRD — GIMME!

WHIT IS THIS, SOME KIND OF JOKE — ?

DON'T PLAY DUMB WITH ME! HAND IT OVER, OR I'LL PUMP MORE HOLES IN YA THAN A SLAB OF GORGONZOLA!

It was heavy — heavier than I expected. And ice cold... like diamonds!

NOW EVERYBODY JUST STAY CALM AN' NOBODY NEED GET HURT!

BLAM!

BLAM! BLAM!

It was a lie, of course. Any one of them could've bought it when I sprayed the place —

SPAANG!

KRAAK!

MURDER, POLIS!

HELP!

GET DOWN!

BLAM!

I hadn't gone fifty yards before I saw lights in my mirror —

I'd picked up a tail.

Of course — the cabbie! He was part of this. He was probably working for the Fat Man.

Come to think of it, I was sure I knew that face.

Those ears... that was it! They had to be stick-ons. Pull them off and five would get you ten you'd be looking at a rat-faced geek called Wilmer.

Yeah — Wilmer. Sure. The creep had played me for a sucker! He knew I'd find the Big-Bird — thought he'd let me handle the rough stuff, then just step in and steal the prize.

Well, finding me and catching me are two different matters entirely — as Wilmer was about to find out.

DON'T WORRY, SWEETHEART. YOU'RE IN SAFE HANDS NOW.

PAT! PAT!

HONK! HONK!

BLOODY NUTTER!

KRUNG!

SCREEEEE

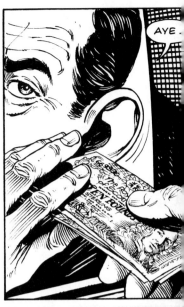

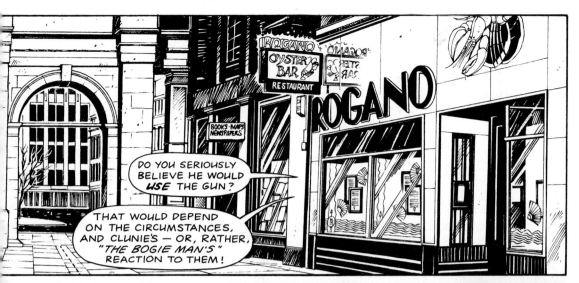

DO YOU SERIOUSLY BELIEVE HE WOULD *USE* THE GUN?

THAT WOULD DEPEND ON THE CIRCUMSTANCES, AND CLUNIE'S — OR, RATHER, *"THE BOGIE MAN'S"* REACTION TO THEM!

BUT YES, YOU COULD SAFELY ASSUME HE WOULDN'T HESITATE TO SHOOT AT ANYONE OR ANYTHING — FOR ANY REASON THAT MIGHT TAKE HIS FANCY.

THAT'S THE TROUBLE WITH TRYING TO PREDICT HIS MOVEMENTS, RAB — THEY'RE TOTALLY RANDOM, THEY FOLLOW NO LOGICAL PATTERN.

GREAT!

NEVER MIND. I'M SURE YOU CAN DO WITH A NIGHT OFF AS MUCH AS I CAN.

IT'S BEEN A LOVELY MEAL, RAB. THANK YOU.

THE PLEASURE'S MINE.

EXCUSE ME, SERGEANT—

HAT? — WHERE? — YOU'RE SURE IT'S *HIM?* — RIGHT, ON MY WAY!

WE'VE GOT OUR ANSWER. THERE'S BEEN A SHOOTING — A BAR IN COWCADDENS.

"THE BOGIE MAN IS ON THE MOVE!"

SCRREEE!

I took the pedestrian mall at 60. But I had to hand it to Wilmer —

— the little geek was sticking to me tighter than Mae West's corsets.

FASTEN YOUR SEATBELT, SWEETHEART. I STILL GOT ONE TRICK UP MY SLEEVE!

LOOK OUT! HE'S DOING A U-TURN!

SKRANGGGG!

I was out of the car faster than a cat in a sling-shot —

LET'S DITCH THE PHONEY EARS, HUH, WILMER!

AAAAH! OWWW!

Don't know what kind of glue he was using. I might've stretched them some, but they sure weren't going anywhere —

NO! AAHHH! PLEASE, MISTER —!

STOP! AAAHH!

FORGET THE EARS, WILMER! ALL THE EARS IN CHINA WON'T SAVE YOU NOW! THIS IS THE END OF THE ROAD — TIME TO BITE THE BULLET — THE BIG KISS OFF...!

NO! PLEASE!

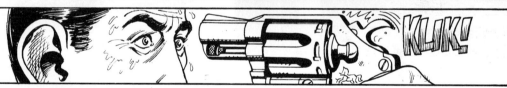

KLIK!

AWWOOOAAWWOOOAAWWOOOAAWW

Sometimes Dame Fortune smiles on a man.

BLATT!

She smiled on Wilmer tonight.

I drove till the wail of the sirens died away in the distance. Then for the first time I gazed upon the splendour of the fabled Maltese Falcon.

It didn't look quite like I'd imagined — then again, I'd never been to Malta.

So this was the priceless treasure men had fought and died over — women had sold their bodies for... the stuff dreams are made of.

The **Big Bird**.

And what's more, there wasn't just one of the little tykes — I had a whole trunkful!

THE BOGIE MAN

™

TO HUV AND HUVNAE

WEEEOOOAAAOOO

POLICE

POL 13

HERE COMES THE POLIS!

YOU TWO'LL BE MY WITNESSES, RIGHT?

AN' WHIT'LL WE SAY WE WITNESSED, BIG EARS? YOU CRASHIN' THE LIGHTS? DRIVIN' THE WRANG WAY DOON A WAN WAY STREET?

SIXTY MPH UP THE PEDESTRIAN PRECINCT?

YOU WANT TAE KEEP THAT LICENCE YE'LL FORGET AW ABOOT WHIT YE'VE BEEN UP TO! AN' FORGET ABOOT THAT SIERRA, TOO!

—BUT WHAT'LL I TELL THEM?

TELL 'EM YER LUGS FELL OWER YER FACE FER AW I CARE — JUS' DON'T MENTION THAT SIERRA!

AN' I'LL HUV MA FIFTY QUID BACK! THAT'S THE WORST TAXI RIDE I EVER HAD!

SKY IT, BOAB!

TO HUV AND HUVNAE

They say every city is a lady — every city has her own charms, her own secrets. You had to wonder about Glasgow. City of Culture, they called it — but so far the only kind of culture I'd found you could grow on a dish.

Still, I could forgive Glasgow a lot tonight. For tonight she'd given up her secret... the priceless treasure I'd crossed four continents to find — the prize the Fat Man would sell his soul to get his greasy hands on...

...the Big Bird.

No, it wasn't quite how I'd imagined the Maltese Falcon.

TINK TINK!

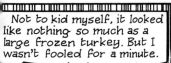

Not to kid myself, it looked like nothing so much as a large frozen turkey. But I wasn't fooled for a minute.

THIS WON'T HURT A BIT, BABE!

Cold, clammy skin on the outside, but I could only guess at the riches I would find underneath...

WHITE MEAT?

BONE?

STUFFING?

THAT BUM IN THE BAR—HE WAS WILLIN' TO GIVE HIS *LIFE* TO STOP YOU GETTIN' YOUR MITTS ON THE BIRD. AN' WILMER...

YEAH... SURE... THE LITTLE CREEP TRIED TO RUN YOU OFF THE ROAD, DIDN'T HE?

ONLY A *LUNATIC* WOULD DO THAT FOR A FROZEN TURKEY!

No, there had to be more to it. Something I couldn't see, some angle I couldn't put my finger on.

But there was no longer any doubt in my mind — this *was* the Big Bird.

A little mutilated, maybe, but there was plenty more where it came from. Each one worth a cool million — if I could only crack its secret...

And it was beginning to look like only one man on this Earth could supply me with the answers — the man who'd already killed seventeen times in his insane quest for the Falcon...

Time I came face to face with the Fat Man.

69

WHAT EXACTLY DID HE SAY TO YOU, MISS —

SKELLY — YVONNE SKELLY.

HE WAS ASKIN' ABOOT WILLIE BROON.

BROON — YOU MEAN *BROWN*?

AYE, BROON. THIS BIG FAT GUY THAT USED TAE COME IN HERE — A RIGHT BIG SLOB HE WUZ.

WHY DID HE WANT TO KNOW ABOUT THIS BROWN?

I'VE NAE IDEA. HE SEEMED INTERESTED IN FAT MEN GENERALLY.

I WUZ JUST SITTIN' HERE LISTENIN' TAE THE MUSIC, OFFICER. "CHIRPY CHIRPY CHEEP CHEEP" — YE KEN IT? IT'S MA FAVOURITE!

OOOOH EEEEE, CHIRPY CHIRPY CHEEP CHEEP —!

GAUN YERSEL', HEN!

NEXT THING I KNOW HE'S BANJOIN' THE MANAGER AN' WAVIN' YON BIG GUN ABOOT! THEN HE GRABS THE TURKEY —

TURKEY? WHAT TURKEY?

THE WAN IN THE BAG.

WHAT BAG?

THE *TESCO* BAG — THE WAN THE BOY HAD.

BOY? *WHAT* BOY?

DON'T KNOW. SOME WEE YAFF IN AFF THE STREET TRYIN' TAE FLOG A FROZEN TURKEY.

ANYWAY, THEN HE STARTS BLAZIN' AWAY AN' RUNS OOT THE DOOR—AN' THE BOY EFTER HIM!

TURKEY...THAT STOLEN LORRY—ANY CONNECTION, D'YOU THINK, GEORGE?

YOUR GUESS IS AS GOOD AS MINE.

SO OUR BOGIE MAN COMES IN HERE, STEALS A TURKEY AND SHOOTS UP THE PLACE. YOU'RE THE PSYCHIATRIST, OLIVE — TELL ME HOW *THAT* FITS INTO HIS FANTASIES.

ANYWAY HE *WANTS* IT TO, I'M AFRAID, RAB.

HIS THOUGHTS FOLLOW NO LOGICAL PATTERN. HE CAN SWITCH FROM ONE SCENARIO INTO ANOTHER WITHOUT EVEN KNOWING IT.

THE FAT MAN — A CHARACTER FROM *"THE MALTESE FALCON."* YET THE INCIDENT OVER THE PIANO...

"CASABLANCA"!

EVERY BOGART FILM, EVERY PULP DETECTIVE NOVEL — THEY'RE ALL JUMBLED TOGETHER IN FRANCIS CLUNIE'S MIND.

ONE THING, THOUGH...

HE HAS A *NAME* FOR HIS FAT MAN NOW — THIS LLIE BROWN. HE MAY WELL TRY TO FOLLOW THAT UP.

HMM...MIGHT BE WORTH KEEPING AN EYE ON HIM.

AND ON THE OTHER HAND, HE'S JUST AS LIKELY TO FORGET ALL ABOUT BROWN AND HIJACK A PLANE TO TIMBUCTOO!

I'M BEGINNING TO UNDERSTAND.

GENERAL STERNWOOD'S ST.

POLICE

Brrringg
Brrringg

Brrringg
Brrringg

WHIT IN THE NAME —?

WHO IS THIS AT THIS TIME —?

WHIT? WHO?

DUGGIE?

I DON'T KNOW WHIT PART O' THE WORLD YOU'RE CALLIN' FROM, BUT HERE IN KELVINSIDE IT IS *THREE A.M.* IN THE MORNING! IF YOUSE HAS WAKENED THE *DRAGON* I AM PERSONALLY GONNAE SAW YER LEGS AFF AT THE KNEE!

YOU *WHIT?*

YOU *WHIT?*

THE SIERRA —?

HE *WHIT?*

WHAT'S THE MATTER, ANGUS? WHAT ARE YOU SHOUTING ABOUT?

SHUT YER FACE A MEENIT, WUMMAN —!

I MEAN — YOU'RE *AWAKE*, MY PRECIOUS...!

WELL, DINNAE YOU WORRY YOUR SWEET LITTLE HEID. JUST A WEE BIT O' BOTHER WI' WAN O' THE MECHANICS. I'M ATTENDIN' TO IT...

YOU PAIR O' BLOODY HALF-WITS! IF YOUSE DON'T HAVE THAT MOTOR BACK BY THE MORNIN' I WOULD STRONGLY RECOMMEND A VISIT TO FATHER McGINNIS —

NO, BAWHEID! HE WILL NOT KNOW WHERE THE CAR IS! HE WILL, HOWEVER, BE ABLE TO READ YOU THE LAST RITES!

WHAT WAS THAT? WHAT WAS THAT ABOUT MY SIERRA?

EH...NOTHING, MY SWEET — JUST A TEENSY PROBLEM WI' THE CLUTCH...I'M AFRAID YE JUST MIGHT NOT GET IT BACK IN THE MORNIN', THOUGH...

IS THAT SO? WELL, I'M GOING TO SALTCOATS TOMORROW. IF MY CAR'S NOT READY THEN I'LL JUST TAKE YOURS.

MA JAGUAR?

NOW HAUD ON! IF YOUSE THINK YOU ARE DRIVIN' MA JAGUAR THEN YOU ARE AFF YER F —

I MEAN...THE JAGUAR? OH, NO...IT'S NOT A LADY'S CAR. YON HEAVY STEERIN' — AN' YER WEE BUM SLIDIN' ABOOT ON THOSE HORRIBLE LEATHER SEATS —

AN' AW THAT WOOD... WHAT IF IT CAUGHT FIRE? OCH, NO, I JUST COULDNAE PUT YE THROUGH THAT.

ANYTHING ELSE, MY LITTLE TATTIE SCONE, YE'VE ONLY TAE ASK...

THEN I'LL JUST TAKE A TAXI!

A TAXI? TAE SALTCOATS?

HIT D'YE WANT TAE O TAE SALTCOATS R ANYWAY? AEBODY IN THEIR GHT MIND ANTS TAE GO O SALTCOATS!

WELL I DO!

WELL THERE'S NAE NEED TAE GO TO THAT EXPENSE. I'LL SEND UP WAN O' MA DRIVERS WI' A COACH.

IF YOU THINK I'M GOING TO SALTCOATS IN A COACH, ANGUS McCURDIE...

Brrringgg
Brrringgg

ALL
RIGHT, ALL
RIGHT...!

OH, IT'S YOU, GEORGE...
WHAT? WHEN?

AND STILL
NO SIGN OF
HIM?

AYE, ALL
RIGHT, SEE YOU
IN HALF AN
HOUR.

MORNING, RAB.

SLEEP WELL?

NEXT TIME YOU
MISS YOUR LAST TRAIN
REMIND ME TO GET A
SOFTER BATH!

THAT WAS GEORGE. THEY FOUND
A COUPLE OF WAITERS TIED UP
IN A HOTEL ROOM. IT WAS
REGISTERED TO A MR. MILES
ARCHER, BUT THE
DESCRIPTION FITS
THE BOGIE MAN.

MILES ARCHER...
BOGART'S PARTNER IN
"THE MALTESE
FALCON".

YES,
THAT MAKES
SENSE.

THEN IT'S TH
ONLY THING
ABOUT THIS
CASE THAT
HAS SO
FAR!

OH, VERY COMICAL, BOAB!

AIRCHIE — DID *YOU* APPRECIATE BOAB'S WEE JOKE THERE?

UNGGGGGG!

I SEE THAT *YOU'RE* NOT LAUGHIN', DUGGIE.

O-OH, NO, MR. McCURDIE! I KNOW WE MESSED UP AGAIN! WE'LL GET RID O' THE LORRY RIGHT NOW—

IN BROAD DAYLIGHT? DOES YOUR HEID BUTTON UP THE BACK OR SOMETHIN'?

DON'T ANSWER THAT — PURELY RHETORICAL.

AIRCHIE —

HUUUURRRRR!

WHAT MADE YOU MINCEBRAINS *THINK* YOU COULD TAKE THE SIERRA ANYWAY?

WE...WE WERE JUST TRYING TO MAKE A FEW QUID ON THE TURKEYS. WE WERE — UNNN — OOT O' POCKET, SEE...

YOU WERE OOT O' POCKET?

I'VE GOT A MAJOR DISTRIBUTOR WAITIN' ON A HUNDRED THOUSAND POUNDS' WORTH O' *VIDEOS* THAT NEVER ARRIVED!

I'VE GOT SOME *HEIDCASE* OUT DRIVIN' ROUND IN MA WIFE'S *SIERRA*!

WHO *WUZ* THIS CLOWN, ANYWAY?

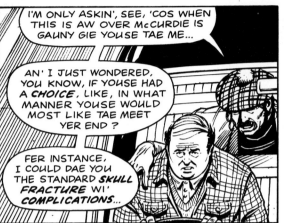

I waited till dark then turned the jalopy towards the club. The dame with the curves — she was my link to the Fat Man. Sooner or later I knew she would show.

I tailed her to the greasy spoon round the corner —

McB

YOU!

Y-YOU KEEP AWAY FRAE ME—!

HAGGIS McMUFFIN £1.50
WEE THOROUS BEASTIE BURGER £1.75
TATTIE McSCONES(3) £1.10
CABER McNUGGET

WHAT'S THE MATTER, SISTER? THOUGHT YOU AN' ME WAS GETTIN' ALONG JUST SWELL LAST NIGHT.

TRY MY NEW HAGGIS BURGER!

AYE — UNTIL YOU PULLED OOT AGUN AN' STARTED BLASTIN'! SOMEBODY COULD'VE BEEN KILLED!

WRONG. EVERY ONE OF THOSE BULLETS WAS CAREFULLY PLACED. MAXIMUM EFFECT, MINIMUM DAMAGE. THAT'S MY STYLE.

B-BUT THE POLIS SAID YOU'RE CRAZY — YOU'VE ESCAPED FRAE THE LOONEY BIN!

SO THAT'S WHAT THEY'RE SAYIN' ABOUT ME, HUH? BELIEVE ME, SWEETHEART, IT'S A LIE!

BUT WHY WOULD THEY LIE?

THEY HAD TO COME UP WITH *SOME* KIND OF COVER STORY. THE FLATFEET DAREN'T RISK ANYONE DISCOVERING THE *REAL* TRUTH ABOUT WHAT'S ON THE LOOSE IN GLASGOW!

I took a look round. Far as I could tell nobody was listening — though the brat in the corner was going to feel the back of my hand if he didn't stop slurping that shake.

SLUUUURRRP-P-P!

LISTEN, YOU GOT THE KIND OF EYES A MAN CAN TRUST. I NEVER DONE IT BEFORE BUT I'M GONNA DO IT NOW — I'M GONNA COME CLEAN WITH YOU.

I'M A PRIVATE EYE.

HERE'S MY CARD.

THAT'S A *MATCHBOOK* FRAE THE BAR!

SO IT IS. MUST BE ALL OUTA CARDS. NEVER MIND.

FACT OF THE MATTER IS, I'VE BEEN WORKING THIS CASE FOR YEARS NOW. I'VE FOLLOWED IT ACROSS FOUR CONTINENTS, A TRAIL SO HOT MY SHOES ARE STILL SMOULDERING. NOW I'VE FOUND IT, HERE IN THIS ONE-HORSE LITTLE BURG.

EVER HEARD TELL OF A LITTLE ITEM CALLED... THE *MALTESE FALCON*?

AYE! DID THEY NO' MAKE A FILM ABOOT THAT?

81

MISTER! WAIT!

I—I SUPPOSE THEY CAN SPARE ME FER THE WAN NIGHT.

HEY, I DON'T EVEN KNOW YOUR NAME. I'M YVONNE.

FOLKS JUST CALL ME... BOGIE.

YOU KNOW, I'M GLAD YOU'RE NO' A LOONEY. I THINK YOU'RE QUITE NICE REALLY, YOU KNOW, DIFFERENT — BUT NICE.

YOU READ ME LIKE A BOOK, SISTER.

'SCUSE —

SLUURRRPPPP!

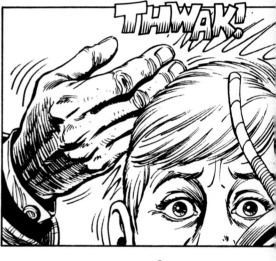

THWAK!

WHAT'S THE MATTER WITH YOU KID — MA NEVER TEACH YOU NO MANNERS?

WAHHHH

Y'KNOW, COME TAE THINK O' IT, IT WUZNAE JUST THE *POLIS* ASKIN' ABOOT WILLIE...

HIS BIG ARDCASE COMES NTAE THE BAR THIS FTERNOON — A IGHT HAIRY GORILLA. E WUZ ASKIN' AW BOOT YOU — ND WILLIE.

SO... SOMEONE ELSE LOOKING FOR THE FAT MAN!

BIG HAIRY GORILLA... COULD BE ANY ONE OF A THOUSAND GUYS I KNOW — A FEW OF THE DAMES AS WELL.

But one thing was sure — the Fat Man's place would be drawing more heat than a new girl at the cathouse. We had to meet on neutral ground

CALL FATS. I'LL TELL YOU WHAT TO SAY.

BUT I DON'T KNOW HIS NUMBER.

LISTEN, SWEETHEART, THIS IS NO TIME TO GET COLD TOOTSIES. YOU'VE COME TOO FAR TO BACK OUT NOW. ARE YOU IN THIS WITH ME OR NOT?

I... I SUPPOSE I COULD TRY DIRECTORY ENQUIRIES...

IS THAT *IT*? THE *MALTESE FALCON*?

CAN I SEE IT?

SOON, BABY. SOON.

THAT WAS THE BARMAID. I...I'VE TO MEET SOMEONE CALLED BOGIE — HALF AN HOUR IN THE NECROPOLIS. I'VE TO COME ALONE AND BRING THE MONEY.

LISTEN, JUST WHAT'S GOIN' ON HERE?

YOU TELL *ME*, WILLIE.

YOU TELT US YOU DIDN'T *KNOW* THE MAN... SO WHIT'S HE DOIN' *PHONIN'* YOU? AN' WHIT'S AW THIS ABOOT *MONEY*?

I DON'T KNOW! I WAS JUST PLAYIN' ALONG LIKE YOU SAID! I'VE NO' GOT ANY MONEY! MY GIRO DOESNAE COME TILL FRIDAY!

I RECKON THERE'S MAIR TAE THIS THAN YOU'RE LETTIN' ON.

85

Somehow it seemed fitting that we should meet here, me and the Fat Man. Here amid the mouldering bones of the dead. How many dreams had perished in pursuit of the Big Bird? How many widows had wept salt tears over its pimpled skin?

But tonight was the end of the trail. Tonight I was walking out of here a rich man —

Or not at all.

AW, GO ON, BOGIE, GIE'S A WEE KEEK!

ALL RIGHT, I GUESS YOU HAVE TO SEE IT SOMETIME.

THERE — HOLD IT IN YOUR HAND.

JINGS! IT'S SHUGE!

TWELVE POUNDS OF MEATY GOODNESS, SWEETHEART.

B-BUT THAT'S NO MALTESE FALCON — IT'S A TURKEY!

DON'T BE FOOLED. I MADE THAT MISTAKE MYSELF.

MEN DON'T DIE FOR A TURKEY.

BUT IT SAYS SO ON THE WRAPPER! TWELVE POUND, OVEN-READY, SAGE AND ONION STUFFED TURKEY!

WHAT DO YOU EXPECT IT TO SAY? "MALTESE FALCON — PRICELESS"?

LIVE IN THE REAL WORLD, BABE.

Y'KNOW, I'M BEGINNIN' TAE WONDER ABOOT YOU AGAIN. I MEAN, WAITIN' IN THE NECROPOLIS AT DEAD O' NIGHT FER WILLIE BROON TAE SHOW UP AN' GIE US MILLIONS O' MONEY — FER A TURKEY?

I MUST BE AFF MA HEID!

DON'T SAY THAT, SWEETHEART! DON'T EVER SAY THAT!

WHEREVER YOU GO IN THIS ROTTEN WORLD YOU'LL FIND PEOPLE TRYIN' TO TELL YOU YOU'RE CRAZY! DON'T EVER LISTEN TO THEM!

DEEP IN YOUR HEART YOU'LL ALWAYS KNOW THE TRUTH, YOU'LL ALWAYS BE SURE OF ONE THING —

YOU'RE EVERY BIT AS SANE AS *I* AM.

THAT'S WHIT I'M WORRIED ABOOT!

ALL TOGETHER NOW — *HEAVE!*

AH! OW! THAT HURTS!

UNGGGG!

FLUMPPP!

HEY'VE GONE INTO THE NECROPOLIS. HERE'S SOMETHING GOING ON ERE, ALL RIGHT. GET ME OME BACK UP!

YOU'VE HEARD A LOT OF THINGS YOU FIND HARD TO BELIEVE. I CAN UNDERSTAND THAT. BUT *I'M* EXPERIENCED IN THESE MATTERS — THIS IS MY WORLD. AND TAKE IT FROM ME, EVERYTHING'S GONNA COME GOOD FOR US TONIGHT.

—PLEASE, MISTER, I'M TELLIN' THE TRUTH! WHATEVER'S GOING ON, I DON'T WANT ANY PART OF IT! I'M ONLY HERE 'COS A BOY WITH A BAT *MADE* ME...!

QUIT THE ACT, FAT MAN! YOU AIN'T WRIGGLIN' OUT ON ME NOW!

I KEPT MY SIDE OF THE BARGAIN! THERE'S THE FALCON — CHECK IT!

BUT... THIS IS JUST A... TURKEY!

YEAH... THAT'S SOMETHIN' I WANTED TO ASK YOU ABOUT —

A gun roared behind me, and the air filled with the acrid stench of cordite —

FRAAAATT!

I-I'M *SORRY*, AIRCHIE! I COULDNAE HELP IT!

YOU ARE *DEID!*

91

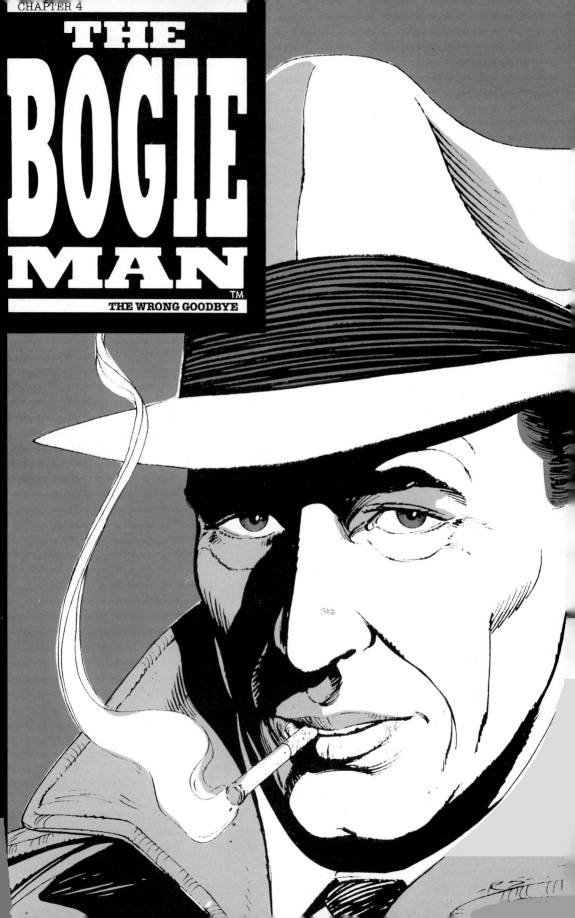

THE BOGIE MAN

TM

THE WRONG GOODBYE

It happened fast and it was dark. At least that's my excuse for missing with the first shot. By number two I'd got his range. Not that it fazed this guy.

My money said one of his parents was a *rhinoceros*.

KACHOW!

The other was a pinch hitter for the Yankees.

KACHOW!

AW HEYYYYYYY—!

UNGGGGG!

FLUMP!

Whoever this big palooka was, something told me he wasn't working for the Fat Man.

YE FAT BASTARD! GERRAFF!

JAB JAB!

THE WRONG GOODBYE

I SEND YOU OOT OAN A SIMPLE WEE ERRAND AN' WHIT DO I GET? THE SIERRA'S A *WRECK*, YE'RE *BLEEDIN'* AW OWER THE PLACE, YE'VE *KILT* A POLISMAN — AN' YE BRING BACK HALF O' GLASGOW TAE BOOT!

WHAT *IS* THIS? ARE WE HAVIN' A *PAIRTY* OR SOMETHIN'?

ER, HELLO, I'M WILLIE BROON. I'VE GOT NOTHING TO DO WITH AW THIS —

YOU! SHUT IT!

FATSO AN' MICKEY ROONEY THERE HAVE GOT SOME KIND O' *SCAM* ON THE GO. HE'S NO' SAYIN' WHIT, BUT I RECKON THERE'S A LOT O' MONEY INVOLVED.

MONEY, YOU SAY? *MONEY?* WELL, THAT *DOES* PUT A DIFFERENT COMPLEXION ON THE MATTER...

WERE YOU BY ANY CHANCE... FOLLOWED?

AYE, MR. McCURDI —AIRCHIE FOLLOWED IN THE MINI-BUS.

APART FROM AIRCHIE, BOAB!

WHIT *IS* IT WI' YOU? WERE YOU *BORN* STUPIT OR DO YOU HAVE TAE *WORK* AT IT?

I GUESS IT — OW! — JUST COMES NATURAL...!

THERE WUZ NAEBODY BEHIND US, AH MADE SURE.

101

BUT HE CANNAE CASH THEM IN WITHOOT THE *FAT MAN* THERE. HE'S A FAMOUS INTERNATIONAL CRIMINAL. HE'S THE ONLY WAN KNOWS THE SECRET O' THE BIG BIRDS.

DADS NOD DRUE!

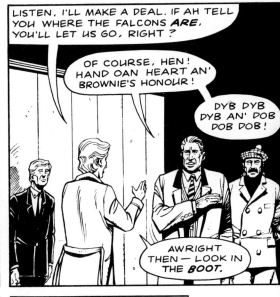

LISTEN, I'LL MAKE A DEAL. IF AH TELL YOU WHERE THE FALCONS *ARE*, YOU'LL LET US GO, RIGHT?

OF COURSE, HEN! HAND OAN HEART AN' BROWNIE'S HONOUR!

DYB DYB DYB AN' DOB DOB DOB!

AWRIGHT THEN — LOOK IN THE *BOOT*.

IT'S THE *TURKEYS*, MR. McCURDIE.

2 MAC.

SO IT'S A *MALTESE FALCON*? AN' THERE WUZ US THINKIN' IT'S A *VIDEO RECORDER*, EH, BOAB?

ER... HA HA, MR. McCURDIE.

CAN WE GO NOO?

NO, HEN. NO' TILL I'VE GOT TAE THE BOTTOM O' THIS.

JUST THE WAN LEFT TAE TRY... AIRCHIE — WAKE HIM UP!

MAYBE WE'LL GET SOME SENSE OOTA *HIM*.

RAB!

OHHH, MY HEID...!

YOU WERE LUCKY — JUST CREASED YOU. ANOTHER INCH TO THE SIDE...

WHAT HAPPENED?

THERE WERE SHOTS... A WOMAN SHOUTED — "BOGIE, RUN"... THEN EVERYTHING WENT BLANK...

THEY WERE HOLDING A MEETING HERE — THE BOGIE MAN AND McCURDIE'S CREW.

WELL, THEY'RE NO' HERE NOW, SARGE. JUST THIS...

THE TURKEY AGAIN! KEEPS TURNIN' UP, EH?

THEY LEFT THIS AS WELL. POINT 38, SAME AS WAS STOLEN FROM CALLAGHAN'S.

YOU OUGHT TO GET THAT LOOKED AT, RAB.

AYE, WHEN THIS IS OVER. I WANT SEARCH WARRANTS ON McCURDIE, HOME AND YARD. AIRCHIE PUDDOCK TOO.

SOMEONE GET ON TO DOCTOR BRANCH AT SPINBINNIE — TELL HER WE'RE CLOSING IN!

WELL *HULLAWRERR!*

FEELIN' REFRESHED AFTER YER WEE NAP, I HOPE.

IF IT'S NO' TOO MUCH TROUBLE I'VE A FEW QUESTIONS TAE ASK — AN' I HOPE FOR YOUR SAKE YOUSE CAN PROVIDE SATISFACTORY ANSWERS, BECAUSE YOU ARE IN DEEP SHITE AWREADY FOR WHIT YOU DID TAE MA WIFE'S *SIERRA*...

TELL HIM WHIT HE WANTS TAE KNOW, BOGIE — THEN WE CAN GET OOTA HERE!

I sized up the situation. It was some kind of transport depot. The Fat Man had his nose in a vice. He was whimpering like a baby. Alarm bells started ringing in my head.

HELLLBBB! PLEEEED HELLLBBBB!

THEY TELL ME THIS HERE IS A *MALTESE FALCON* AND IT'S WORTH A CONSIDERABLE SUM OF MONEY. NOO IF THIS IS SO I WOULD LIKE TAE KNOW ABOOT IT, BECAUSE IT JUST SO HAPPENS I AM SITTIN' ON A WHOLE *LORRYLOAD* O' THEM!

WAR
UNLA
NOTT
ENSL
GILLI

Say what you like about the Fat Man, one thing was for sure, he was always cool under pressure. That quivering lump of jello over there — he was no more the Fat Man than I'm Tom Mix's sister.

MR. McCURDIE IS *TALKIN'* TAE YOU, BAWHEID!

UNFFFF!

How could I have let myself be suckered for so long? A little older — a little greyer round the temples maybe — but there was no mistaking that voice, that air of command...

WELL? WHIT'VE YE GOT TAE SAY?

JUST ONE THING —

LOST A LITTLE WEIGHT, HUH, FAT MAN?

EH?

I DON'T THINK WE'RE ON QUITE THE SAME WAVELENGTH HERE, JAMES —

DON'T GIMME THAT BALONEY, FAT MAN! THE JIG'S UP! I FOLLOWED THE TRAIL AND THE TRAIL ENDS HERE!

YEAH, I SEE IT ALL NOW... I SEE YOUR DEVIOUS MIND BEHIND EVERYTHING! YOU SET THE WHOLE THING UP, DIDN'T YOU?

THAT MATCHBOOK I TOOK FROM McGURK — THE ONLY CLUE AN' IT LED STRAIGHT HERE, IT WAS A PLANT, WASN'T IT? YOU WANTED ME TO TURN UP AT TOMMY TROTTERS! THAT'S WHY YOU SENT YOUR GOONS TO KILL ME AT THE FLOPHOUSE!

NO! WAIT A MINUTE...

THAT CAN'T BE RIGHT.

TRY THIS FOR SIZE — — THE MATCHBOOK WASN'T A PLANT. I WASN'T MEANT TO SEE IT, WAS I? THAT'S WHY YOU SENT YOUR GOONS TO RUB ME OUT, 'COS YOU KNEW WHAT I'D FIND THERE — RATSO WITH THE BIRD!

ARE WE LIVIN' OAN THE SAME PLANET?

A WEE RAP WI' THE BAT 'LL BRING HIM DOON TAE EARTH.

PEOPLE LOSE TEETH TALKIN' TA ME LIKE THAT, PAL.

COME TO THINK OF IT, REAL CONVENIENT RATSO TURNIN' UP LIKE THAT. TOO CONVENIENT...ALMOST AS IF YOU DID WANT ME TO STEAL THE DINGUS...

OF COURSE! YOU NEEDED A PATSY, DIDN'T YOU? SOME SAP TO TAKE THE RAP WHILE YOU AN' THE BOYS WERE HIGHTAILIN' IT FOR THE BORDER WITH YOUR BOOTY!

NO, THAT CAN'T BE RIGHT EITHER... UNLESS...UNLESS THE MATCHBOOK WAS A PLANT... IN WHICH CASE THE ATTEMPTS ON MY LIFE... SET-UPS, YEAH... THEY MUSTA BEEN SET-UPS TOO...

BUT IF THAT'S THE CASE HOW DID WILMER KNOW WHERE TO PICK ME UP? AND THE FROGFACE DAME — WHY'D SHE TRY TO CHARGE ME TWENNY FINS FOR THE ROOM?

NO, NO, THAT DON'T MAKE SENSE...

ET'S SAY THE MATCHBOOK *WAS* PLANT, OKAY? BUT NOT FOR E. IT ONLY *BECAME* A PLANT RETROSPECT.

HAT MEANS THE TS ON ME WEREN'T EANT FOR ME. THEY HOUGHT I WAS SOME- ODY ELSE. IT'S ONLY HEN THEY FOUND UT IT *WAS* ME THAT HEY STARTED UNNING FOR ME— ETROSPECTIVELY PEAKIN'...

NLESS... AIT A MINUTE...

AH, THE HELL WITH IT! YOU WANNA KNOW WHAT THE *REAL* GIVEAWAY WAS, FAT MAN?

THAT WHINING TUB OF LARD OVER THERE—THE *PHONEY* FAT MAN! I GOTTA HAND IT TO YOU, THAT WAS YOUR MASTER TOUCH! THAT'S WHEN I SHOULDA *KNOWN* IT WAS YOU!

HELLLBBBBBBB!

SO THE ONLY THING I NEED TO KNOW NOW, FAT MAN, IS *WHY?*

WHAT IS IT ABOUT THESE BIRDS MAKES THEM SO VALUABLE? WHAT *IS* THE *SECRET* OF THE *MALTESE FALCON?*

IT MAY HAVE ESCAPED YOUR NOTICE BUT THAT IS EXACTLY WHAT *I* AM ASKIN' *YOU!*

I DON'T GIVE TWA HOOTS *WHIT* FANCY NAME YOU CALL IT, THAT IS JUST A BLOODY *TURKEY!*

SAME OLD FAT MAN, HUH? CAN'T COME CLEAN ABOUT ANYTHING. GOTTA PLAY THE GAME TO THE BITTER END.

Then it hit me like a brick sandwich. I almost wept. I'd been looking for complications when it was all so simple. It'd been staring me in the face all the time!

TURKEY! OF COURSE! WHAT DO YOU *GET* FROM TURKEY?

DRUMSTICKS?

WHITE MEAT?

O! TURKEY HE *COUNTRY!*

TURKISH DELIGHT?

YEAH, YEAH, SURE, TURKISH DELIGHT—BUT WHAT *ELSE?*

DONER KEBABS?

NO!

110

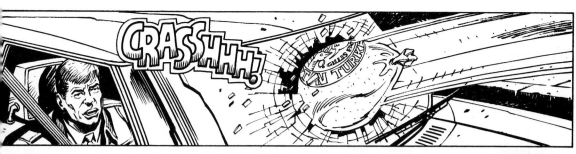

IN FACT, THERE ISN'T ANY.

BUT AT LEAST I CAN DO ONE THING FOR YOU. I CAN MAKE SURE *YOU* COME OUT OF THIS WHOLE ROTTEN BUSINESS *CLEAN*.

BUT AH'VE NO' *DONE* ANYTHING WRANG, BOGIE!

SINCE WHEN HAS THAT EVER STOPPED YOU PAYIN' THE PRICE? NO, THERE'S STILL A RECKONING TO COME, SWEETHEART, BUT WHEN IT DOES YOU AIN'T GONNA BE HERE.

SO WHERE AM AH GONNAE *BE*?

OHMAGOD—!

SCREEEEE

KRANGGGG!

I'M PUTTIN' YOU ON A TRAIN.

115

OLIVE! WHAT'RE YOU DOING THERE?

WHAT DO YOU THINK I'M DOING? I'M STUCK!

THE BOGIE MAN—?

PLATFORM 7!

I'VE HAD ENOUGH O' THIS! I'M GETTIN' AFF!

NO!

LIEVE ME, IF THIS TRAIN AVES AND YOU'RE NOT ON IT U'LL REGRET IT. MAYBE NOT DAY, MAYBE NOT TOMORROW— T SOON AND FOR THE REST OF YOUR LIFE.

WHIT ARE YE HAVERIN' ABOOT NOO?

VICTOR? CONCENTRATION CAMP? CARSTAIRS? PHONEY FAT MAN— BIG BIRDS! NOTHIN' YOU SAY MAKES ANY SENSE, BOGIE!

I'M RAPIDLY COMIN' TAE THE CONCLUSION THE POLIS WUZ RIGHT ABOOT YOU! YOU ARE ROOND THE TWIST— AFF YER CHUMP— YER HEID IS FULLA BROKEN BOTTLES!

YE KEN WHIT AH MEAN? YOU ARE TOTALLY RADIO RENTAL!

THE WORLD'S CRAZY, SWEETHEART— BUT IT DOESN'T TAKE MUCH TO SEE THAT THE PROBLEMS OF THREE LITTLE PEOPLE DON'T AMOUNT TO A HILL OF BEANS.

THREE?

THAT'S WHY YOU GOTTA STAY ON THIS TRAIN. SOMEDAY YOU'LL UNDERSTAND. IN THE MEANTIME...

Yeah, there was still a reckoning to come. But as I turned towards the waiting throng I remembered something Miles Archer, my ex-partner, used to say...

He used to say: "Bogie — three things a good shamus should always remember..."

"One — never give a sucker an even break."

"Two — never trust a kid with shifty peepers."

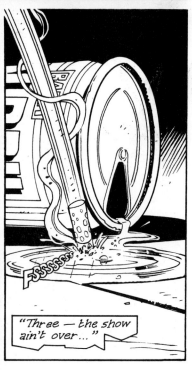

"Three — the show ain't over..."

"...till the fat lady sings."

Whatever the hell
that means!

THE END ?

McGLOSSARY

a': of

aboot: about

aff: off

affy: awfully

afore: before

ah: I

ane: one

annat: "and that". Often mystifyingly used to end a statement, eg – "Ah could fair murder some o' thae chups annat" (I am desirous of having some of those french fries). Totally meaningless.

auld: old

aw: all

awa: away

awright/awricht: alright

aye: yes

bampot: idiot

banjo: strike violently

Bar-L: Barlinnie Prison

baw: ball

bawheid: "ball head". Term of abuse.

baw's up oan the slates: activity is at an end

Bhoys, ra: Glasgow Celtic F.C.

bide: remain

bowfin': stinking

braw: handsome

bricht: bright

brither: brother

but: See "annat". Another word puzzlingly used to close a sentence, eg – "Get yer ain chups, but" (kindly obtain your own french fries).

ca'ed: called

cannae: cannot

china: pal

chump, aff yer: head, off your

claes: clothes

clarty: dirty, smelly

c'm'oan: come on

couldnae: couldn't

dae: do

deid: dead

dinna/dinnae: don't

doon: down

drappa: drop of

dunt: knock, blow

eejit: idiot

efter: after

efternoon: afternoon

Embra: Edinburgh

erse: rear end

eyefu': eyeful

fandabbadozey: fantastic

fer/fur: for

ferrit face: someone about to be struck

frae: from

galoot: stupid fellow

gang: go

gaun: go on

gauny/gonnae: going to

gerra: get the

gerraff: get off

gerrintaeum: "get into them". Attack with some vigour.

gie: give

gie's: give us

greet: cry

hame: home

haud: hold

hauns: hands

haverin': prattling

heid: head

heidbanger: dangerous lunatic

heidcase: ordinary, everyday lunatic

heid-the-baw: Literally "head the ball". An idiot.

help ma boab: expression of alarm, literally "help me Robert"

hen: term of affection

Hogmanay: New Year's Eve

hoo: how

ose: house
llawrerr: hello there
iv: have
ivnae: have not
tae: into
her: other
ikit: jacket
mmy: anyone (male) you don't
now
ngs: exclamation
eek: glance, look
en: know
lt: killed
ldy: a thrashing
ng syne: long ago, long since
gs: ears
a: my
air: more
airrit: married
eenit: minute
ichty me: exclamation; – eg
od grief!
ickey Rooney: loony (rhyming
ang)
oonlicht: moonlight/lit
ooth: mouth
urder, polis!: exclamation of
arm
ae: no
ae tother a ba': no bother at all
ebody: nobody
aw: no
cht: night
': not
o: how
tter: maniac
aff: person of no account
 of
n: on
h: roughly equivalent to "oh".
onounce as if clearing the
roat.
the batter: drinking heavily
r: our
t/oota: out/out of
ver: over
irty: party

Partick Thistle: Scottish football
team
piece: sandwich
polis: police
ra: the
radio rental: mental (rhyming
slang)
roond: round
Saltcoats: once popular Scottish
seaside resort
sangwidge: sandwich
screw the nut: get a grip of
yourself
shuge: huge
sky it: run for it
soash: social security
stoater: particularly fine example
of anything
stupit: stupid
sufferin' duck: exclamation of
displeasure
tae: to, too
tak: take
tattie: potato
telt: told
thae: those
twa: two
Vindaloo: hot curry
wan: one
weans: children
wha: who
whit/whut: what
wi': with
wifie: wife
withoot: without
wrang: wrong
wumman: woman
wuz/wuznae: was/was not
ya/ye: you
yer: your
yersel': yourself
yin: one
yon: that
youse: you (usually plural)

SPINNBINNIE HOSPITAL

INMATE REPORT N°: 38567/A1
FOR ATTENTION OF: Dr. O. BR

INMATE: Wagner, John
D.O.B. Unknown
AGE: 41 (approx)
PLACE OF BIRTH: Pennsylvania, USA
CASE HISTORY: Showed early signs of living a double life when as a bulky second-row he fantasised about playing wing-forward in the school rugby team. "I should have been allowed to run free," he told his bewildered games master. First came to our notice as a sub-editor at Dundee-based publishers, DC Thomson, trying to insert subliminal messages into a horoscope he wrote for th local paper. Over the last 15 years has become obsessed with what he sees as the coming nuclear apocalypse in writings (many with partner, Grant) such as JUDGE DREDD (Fleetway) and THE LAST AMERICAN (Epic).

INMATE: Grant, Alan
D.O.B. Unknown
AGE: 41 (approx)
PLACE OF BIRTH: Bristol, England
CASE HISTORY: After re-locating to Edinburgh at an early age, Grant swiftly came to our attention as a troublemaker at school – asked to take part in psychiatric tests, he refused. Then, announcing his presence clad in a smelly (Afghan coat, Grant joined Wagner at DC Thomson, before moving down to London where he enjoyed a brief reign as 'The Puzzle King of Fleet Street'. Ha lately shown a morbid interest in violent fantasy, writing BATMAN (DC), LOB (DC) and, with Wagner, JUDGE DREDD (Fleetway).

INMATE: Smith, Robin
D.O.B: 7/02/57
PLACE OF BIRTH: Port Sunlight, England
CASE HISTORY: The most promising of the three cases under review here, Sm had a trouble-free childhood. Showed early evidence of a talent for drawing w he attended art college for three years at the tail end of the seventies. It was only later, working as Art Editor on 2000 AD, that he started to show some (the same anti-social tendencies as Wagner and Grant. A brief break from thei corrupting influence was made when Smith tried his and at illustrating com strips for crisp packets.

REPORT PREPARED
BY *[signature]*
AND DATED 31/7

IF THE STRAIT-JACKET FITS...

WEAR IT!

t was a long hot summer night. So hot the steam was rising up from the road the vay cordite floats up from a piece after it's been fired. Just my luck, all I had to vear was the same old raincoat I'd had since Chinatown was a place that Chinamen ived in and not just somewhere gangsters went to eat. Waterproof, but I could see it vasn't gonna rain until the Fat Lady sang. I needed a change. Then I spotted them 'ishing out my mugshot in every sleazy bar, run-down poolroom and cut-price aberdashers in the city. Every piece of lowlife was crawling out into the street with ny face pasted onto their chest on a T-shirt. I couldn't believe it. Though I gotta .ay, it looked kinda sharp, so I took one for myself.

.o if you wanna get yours, all you need to do is mail a cheque or postal order for ,7.99 to: **Bogie Man T-shirt Offer, John Brown Publishing, The Boathouse, Crabtree .ane, London SW6 8NJ**. (Overseas suckers add 20% of order value). And don't be a chmuck, remember to photocopy the form, fill in your name and address, and llow 28 days for delivery. One size, XL, fits any frozen turkey.